Essex County Council

Many libraries in Essex have
facilities for exhibitions
and meetings —

enquire at your local library
for details

The Complete Rock & Pop Guitar Player

by Mick Barker, Rick Cardinali, Roger Day.

Book 1

Songs and music in this book

Wise Publications
London/New York/Paris/Sydney/Copenhagen/Madrid

The Guitar

Whether you have an acoustic or an electric guitar, the principles of playing are fundamentally the same, and so are most of the features on both instruments. In order to 'electrify' an acoustic guitar (as in the diagram), a magnetic pick-up can be attached to those guitars with steel strings or a 'bug' style microphone pick-up can be attached to guitars with nylon strings. If in doubt check with your local music shop.

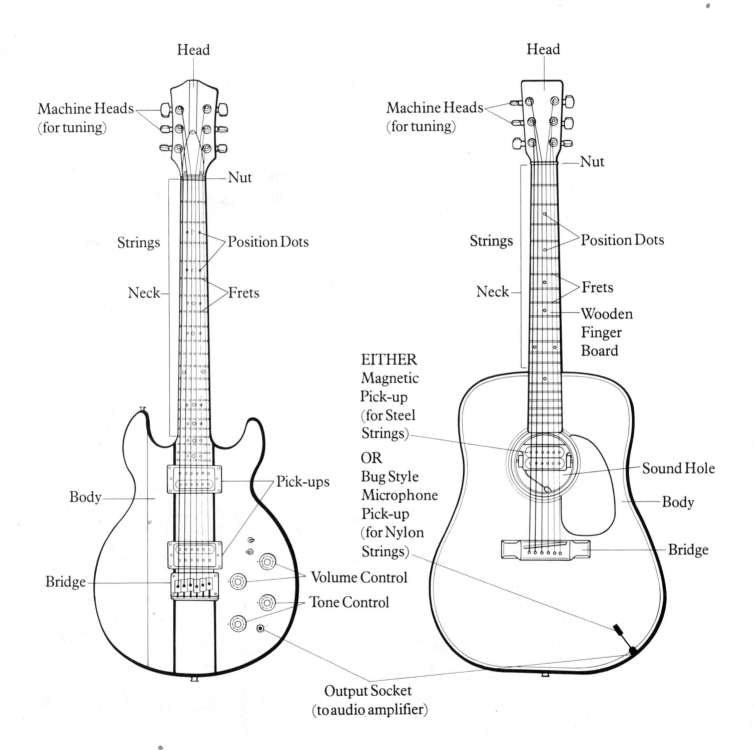

Holding The Guitar

The picture above shows a comfortable position for playing rock or pop guitar

The Right Hand

When STRUMMING (brushing your fingers across the strings), hold your fingers together.

When PICKING (plucking strings individually), hold your wrist further away from the strings than for strumming. Keep your thumb slightly to the left of your fingers which should be above the three treble strings as shown.

The Plectrum

Many modern guitar players prefer to use a plectrum to strike the strings. Plectrums come in many sizes, shapes and thicknesses and all are available from your local music shop. Start with a fairly large, soft one if possible, with a grip. The photo shows the correct way to hold your plectrum.

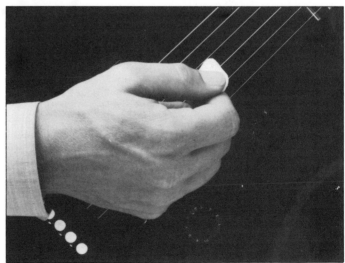

Left Hand

Use your finger tips to press down the strings in the positions described in this book. Your thumb should be behind your 1st and 2nd fingers pressing on the middle of the back of the neck.

3

Tuning

Accurate tuning of the guitar is essential and is achieved
by winding the machine heads up or down.
It is always better to tune 'up' to the correct pitch
rather than down. Therefore,
if you find that the pitch of your string is
higher (sharper) than the correct pitch,
you should 'wind' down below the correct
pitch and *then* 'tune up' to it.

Relative Tuning

Tuning the guitar to itself without the aid of a pitch
pipe or other tuning device.

Other Methods of Tuning

Pitch pipe
Tuning fork
Dedicated electronic guitar tuner

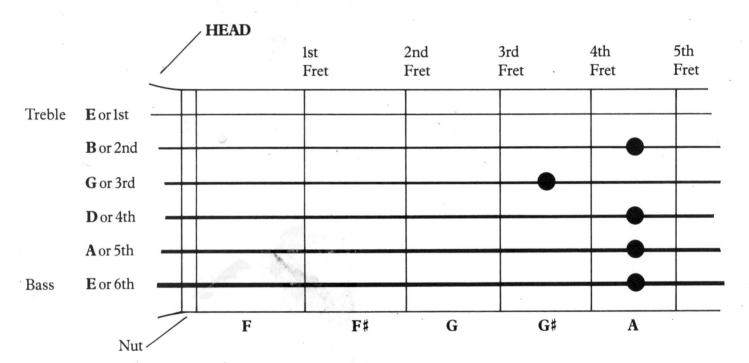

Press down where indicated, one at a time, following the instructions below.

Estimate the pitch of the 6th string as near as possible to
E or at least a comfortable pitch (not too high, as you
might break other strings in tuning up).

Then, while checking the various positions on the
above diagram, place a finger from your left hand on:

the 5th fret of the E or 6th string and **tune the open A** (or 5th string) to the note (A)

the 5th fret of the A or 5th string and **tune the open D** (or 4th string) to the note (D)

the 5th fret of the D or 4th string and **tune the open G** (or 3rd string) to the note (G)

the 4th fret of the G or 3rd string and **tune the open B** (or 2nd string) to the note (B)

the 5th fret of the B or 2nd string and **tune the open E** (or 1st string) to the note (E)

Chord Boxes

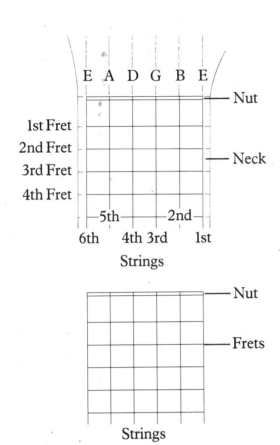

THE FIRST CHORD

The **A** Chord.

The **A** Chord

x = Do not play this string

All chords are major chords unless otherwise indicated.

Left Hand

Place all three fingers into position and press down firmly. Keep your thumb around the middle back of the neck and directly behind your 1st and 2nd fingers.

CHORD BOXES are diagrams of the guitar neck viewed head upwards, face on, as illustrated in the above drawings. The horizontal double line at the top is the nut, the other horizontal lines are the frets. The vertical lines are the strings starting from E or 6th on the left to E or 1st on the right.

Any dots with numbers inside them simply indicate which finger goes where. Any strings marked with an X must not be played.

The fingers of your hand are numbered 1,2,3, & 4 as in the diagram below.

Right Hand Thumb or Plectrum

Slowly play each string, starting with the 5th or A string and moving up to the 1st or E string. IF THERE IS ANY BUZZING, PERHAPS YOU NEED TO:–
Position your fingers nearer the metal fret (towards you);
or adjust the angle of your hand;
or check that the buzz is not elsewhere on the guitar by playing the open strings in the same manner.

Finally, your nails may be too long, in which case, you are pressing down at an extreme angle and therefore not firmly enough. Also, the pad of one of your fingers may be in the way of the next string for the same reason.

So cut your nails to a more comfortable length and then try to keep them as near vertical to the fretboard as possible.

Once you have a 'buzz free' sound, play the chord a few times and then remove your fingers and repeat the exercise until your positioning is right instinctively.

Now turn the page.

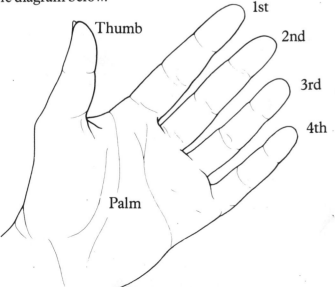

Mull of Kintyre
Words and Music: McCartney/Laine

The **D** Chord

The **D** Chord

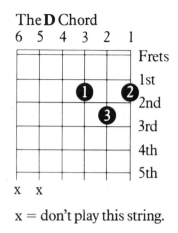

x = don't play this string.

strings from bass **A** (or 5th string) to the treble **E** (or 1st string). Alternatively do the same thing holding your plectrum as shown previously. Then strum this rhythm using down strokes, signified by a downward arrow. Try to keep your strums evenly spaced.

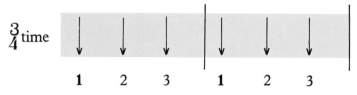

Place your fingers in the correct positions and press down firmly. Remember to keep your thumb around the middle back of the neck and directly behind your 1st and 2nd fingers.

Then follow the same procedure as you did for the **A** chord. This time starting from the 4th (D) string.

Now, are you able to play both chords clearly and cleanly every time? GOOD.

Next, hold down the **A** chord and, keeping the fingers of your *right hand* together, brush your nails down the

Well, if you want to sound technical, you can say you have just played your first two bars of 3/4 time.

Basically, '3/4 (three-four) time' means three beats in a bar, these bars are separated by a bar line which means the end of one bar and the beginning of another.

Now, still holding down your **A** chord, practise changing to **D** with your 'three in a bar' rhythm, this time accentuating the first strum of every bar. It is best to play slowly and evenly at first, so that you have time to change chords without stopping.

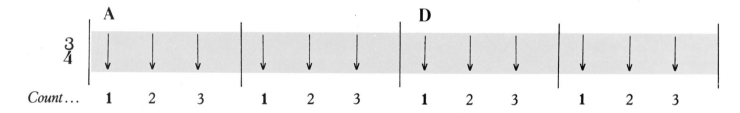

Take note that, at the beginning of the last line of music for this song, you will see the letter 'E'. At this stage, simply strike the bass 'E' or 6th string once, and let the open string sound or 'ring' for the 3 beats of that bar.

Later on in the book you will be given the 'E' chord, which you can substitute for the single note 'E' once you have progressed to that stage.

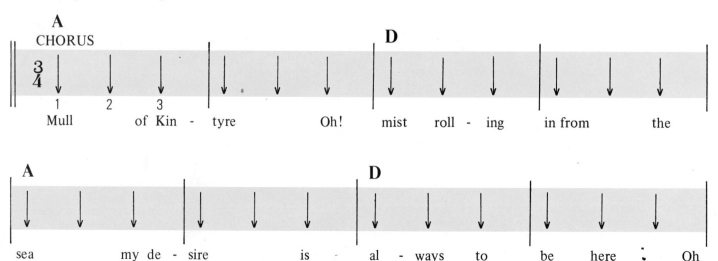

6

Mull of Kintyre   Continued

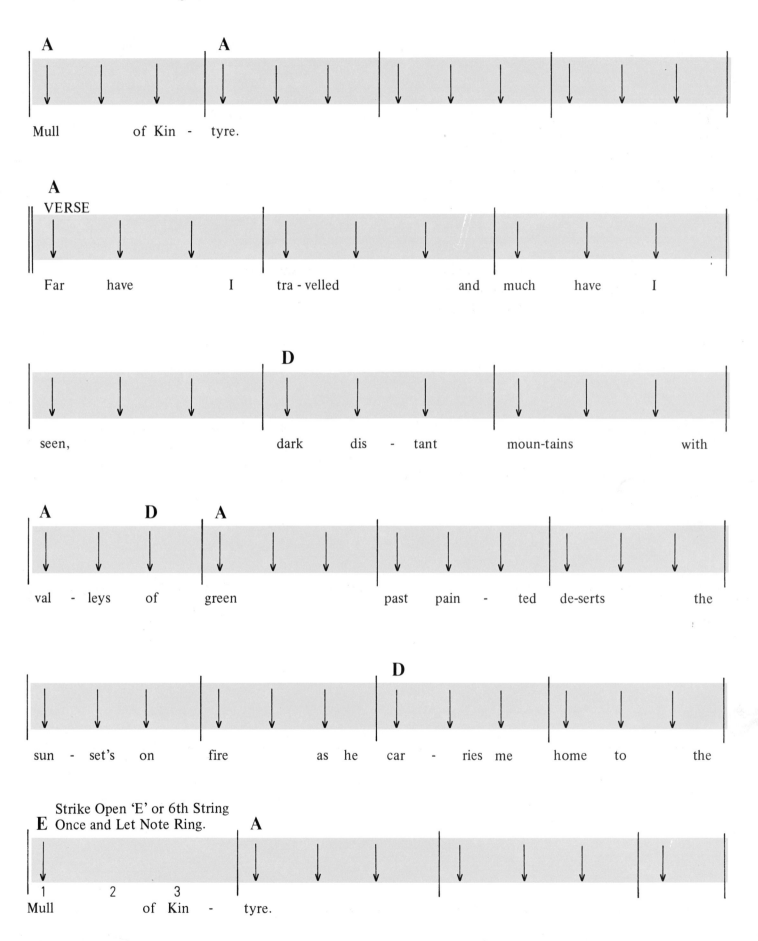

A   **A**

Mull   of Kin - tyre.

A   VERSE

Far have I tra - velled and much have I

D

seen, dark dis - tant moun-tains with

A   **D**   **A**

val - leys of green past pain - ted de-serts the

D

sun - set's on fire as he car - ries me home to the

E Strike Open 'E' or 6th String Once and Let Note Ring. **A**

1   2   3
Mull   of Kin - tyre.

N.B. The full lyric for each song can be found at the back of the book.

© Copyright 1977 by MPL Communications Ltd.
Administered by MPL Communications Ltd, by
arrangement with ATV Music Ltd.
All rights reserved. International copyright secured.

Tom Hark   Music: R. Bopape. New Lyrics: Bob Grover

Now it's time for you to learn your second tune. It's a piece which was a smash hit for The Piranhas and is called 'Tom Hark'. You don't need to learn any new chords for this tune but you are going to learn a new strumming pattern.

The first piece you learnt, 'Mull Of Kintyre', was played in Waltz or 3/4 time and has 3 beats in each bar with one strum for each beat. 'Tom Hark' has 4 beats to each bar (this is called 4/4 time) and we're going to play two strums for each beat. If you look at the first bar you'll see 1 & 2 etc. written under the words. Tap your foot four times in each bar and on the first tap count '1 &', on the second tap count '2 &' and so on. The number is the

down stroke and the '&' is the up stroke.

There's only one more thing to learn and then you can get on with playing the song. This piece of music is written in a swing or shuffle style which means you make the down stroke long and the up stroke short (long and short in this instance refer to time not distance). Try it over a few times and you'll see what is meant.

N.B. For those with some musical knowledge the strums could have been written ⌐ etc. – but that will be explained in later books.

SWING/SHUFFLE

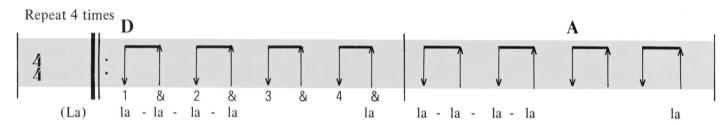

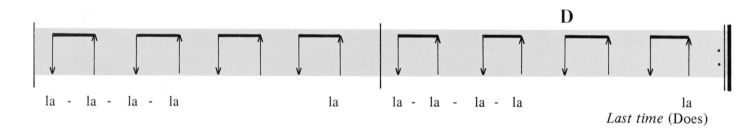

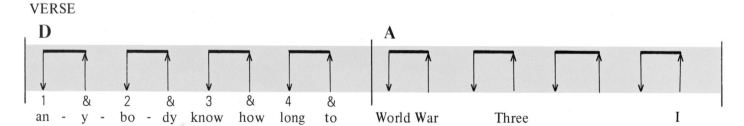

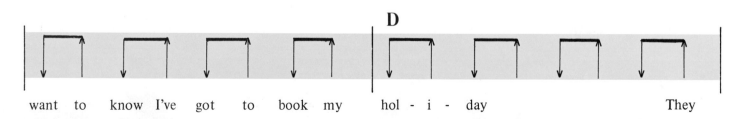

8

Tom Hark Continued

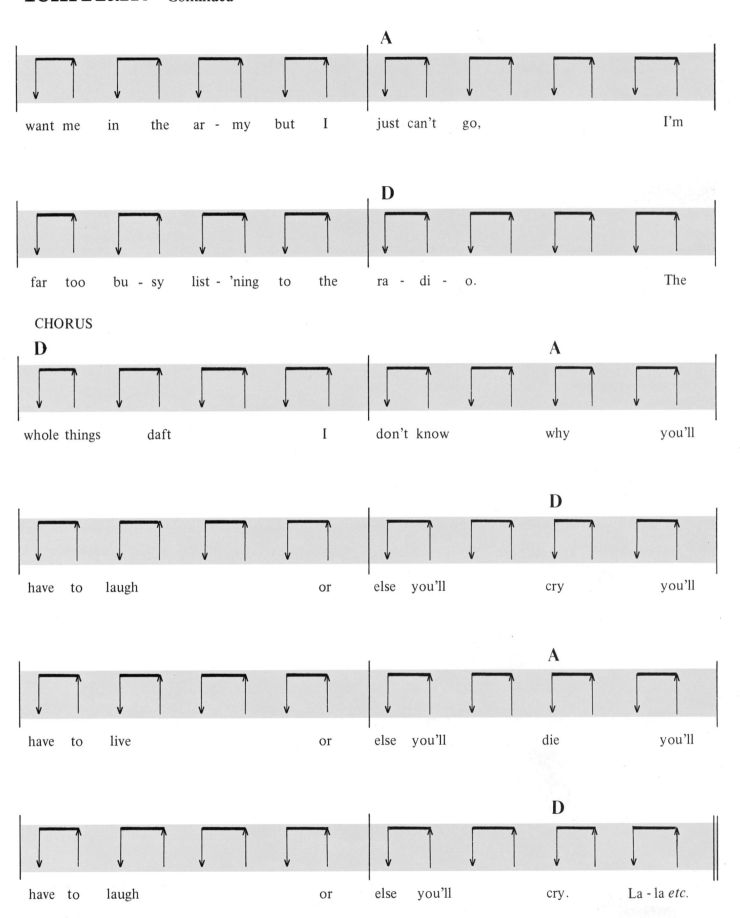

A

want me in the ar - my but I just can't go, I'm

D

far too bu - sy list - 'ning to the ra - di - o. The

CHORUS

D **A**

whole things daft I don't know why you'll

D

have to laugh or else you'll cry you'll

A

have to live or else you'll die you'll

D

have to laugh or else you'll cry. La - la *etc*.

N.B. The full lyric for each song can be found at the back of the book.

© Copyright 1958 EMI (South Africa) Pty. Ltd., Johannesburg.
© Copyright 1980 Southern Music Publishing Co. Ltd., 8 Denmark Street, London W C2.
All rights reserved. International copyright secured.

Summertime Blues   Words & Music: Eddie Cochran & Jerry Capehart

The **E** Chord

The **E** Chord

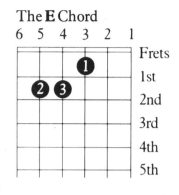

Now you are going to learn your first six-string chord, the chord of **E**. We're going to use it in that classic rock 'n' roll song 'Summertime Blues', originally recorded by Eddie Cochran.

Study the chord box and photo and try playing the chord. As always, play each string separately at first to make sure each note is sounding clearly. Then try strumming full up and down strokes.

Each time you learn a new chord it is a good idea to practise changing smoothly between all the chords you know.

A very good tip: when changing from **E** to **D** or **D** to **E** don't take all your fingers off the strings. The first finger can slide up and down between the first and second frets and makes a good reference point. Try it and you'll see what is meant.

This is not a shuffle song like 'Tom Hark'. Although the timing of the strum pattern looks the same, make all the strokes even. This is called 'straight eight style', because there are eight even strums to a bar.

Finally, in the short instrumental sections notice what a different sound you get by playing four down strokes followed by two up and down strokes. It may take a little practice but it's well worth it. O.K., now you're ready to sing along with Eddie Cochran and 'Summertime Blues'.

STRAIGHT EIGHTS

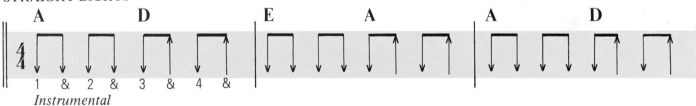

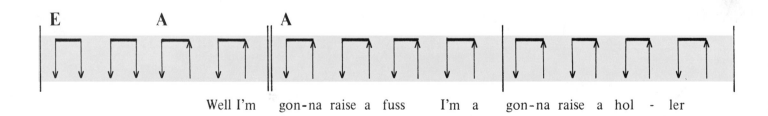

10

Summertime Blues Continued

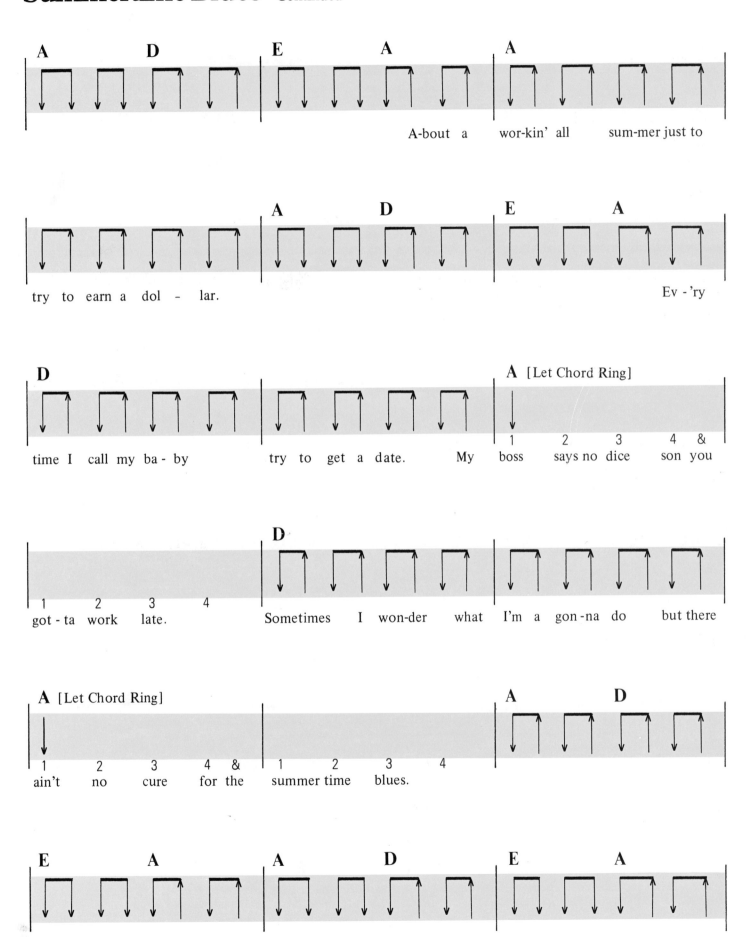

A   D   E   A   A

A-bout a   wor-kin' all   sum-mer just to

A   D   E   A

try to earn a dol – lar.   Ev - 'ry

D   A [Let Chord Ring]

time I call my ba - by   try to get a date. My   boss   says no dice   son you

D

1   2   3   4

got - ta work late.   Sometimes I won-der what I'm a gon-na do   but there

A [Let Chord Ring]   A   D

1   2   3   4   &   1   2   3   4

ain't   no   cure   for the   summer time   blues.

E   A   A   D   E   A

N.B. The full lyric for each song can be found at the back of the book.

Hello I Love You

Words & Music: The Doors

The **G** Chord

The **G** Chord

```
6  5  4  3  2  1
              Frets
              1st
       1
              2nd
   2          3
              3rd
              4th
              5th
```

The **C** Chord

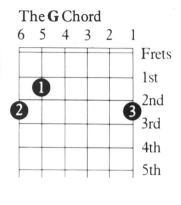

The **C** Chord

```
6  5  4  3  2  1
                 1  Frets
              2     1st
                    2nd
    3               3rd
                    4th
                    5th
x
```

To play the **G** chord, start by placing your 1st finger on the 2nd fret of the 5th string and then locate the other finger positions.

For the **C** chord, start by placing your 1st finger on the 1st fret of the 2nd string and then locate the other positions.

Remember to play only the top five strings and keep your fingers as near to vertical as possible, so that the pads of your fingers don't interfere with the ringing of adjacent strings.

'Hello I Love You' was a monster hit for the Doors, featuring the great Jim Morrison on vocals. The 'down up' strum pattern is easy to play and the vocals are easy to sing.

STRAIGHT EIGHTS

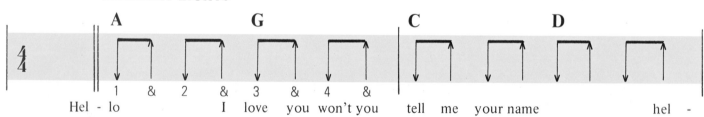

A — G — C — D

1 & 2 & 3 & 4 &

Hel - lo I love you won't you tell me your name hel -

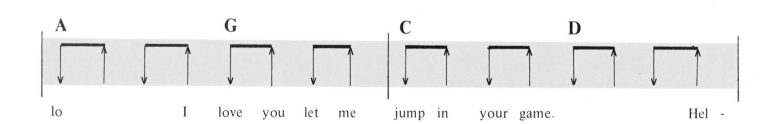

A — G — C — D

lo I love you let me jump in your game. Hel -

12

Hello, I Love You Continued

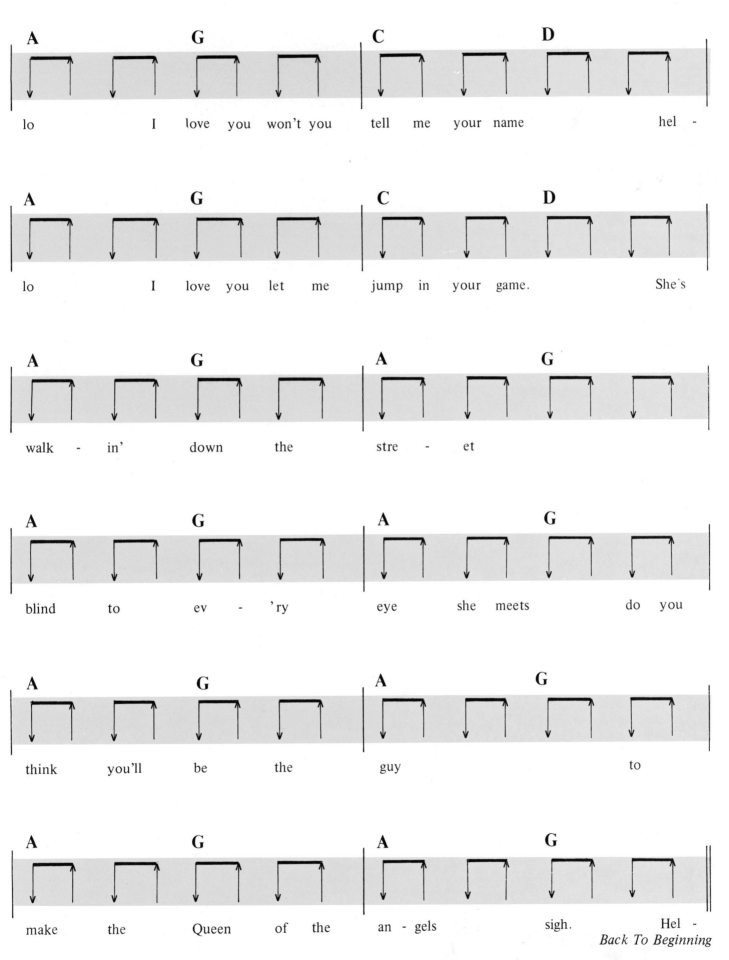

A   G   C   D

lo   I love you won't you   tell me your name   hel -

A   G   C   D

lo   I love you let me   jump in your game.   She's

A   G   A   G

walk - in' down the   stre - et

A   G   A   G

blind to ev - 'ry   eye she meets do you

A   G   A   G

think you'll be the   guy   to

A   G   A   G

make the Queen of the   an - gels sigh.   Hel -
Back To Beginning

N.B. The full lyric for each song can be found at the back of the book.

© Copyright 1968 Doors Music Co.
Rondor Music (London) Ltd., 10a Parsons Green,
London SW 6 for the UK and Eire.
All rights reserved. International copyright secured.

Get Off Of My Cloud
Words & Music: Mick Jagger & Keith Richard

This was a big hit for The Rolling Stones and you don't have to learn any new chords to play it.

To get the right feel for this song, make the first and third beats of each bar heavier than the others. In almost every bar the chord changes on the first and third beats so you'll find it very easy to play.

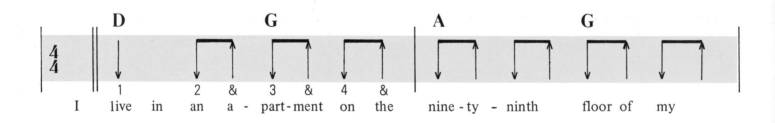

I live in an a - part - ment on the nine - ty - ninth floor of my

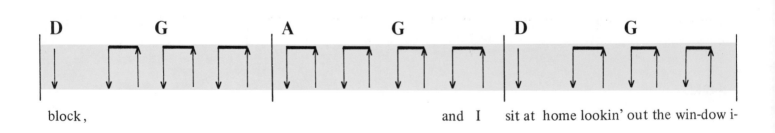

block, and I sit at home lookin' out the win-dow i-

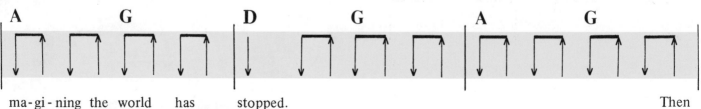

ma - gi - ning the world has stopped. Then

14

Get Off Of My Cloud Continued

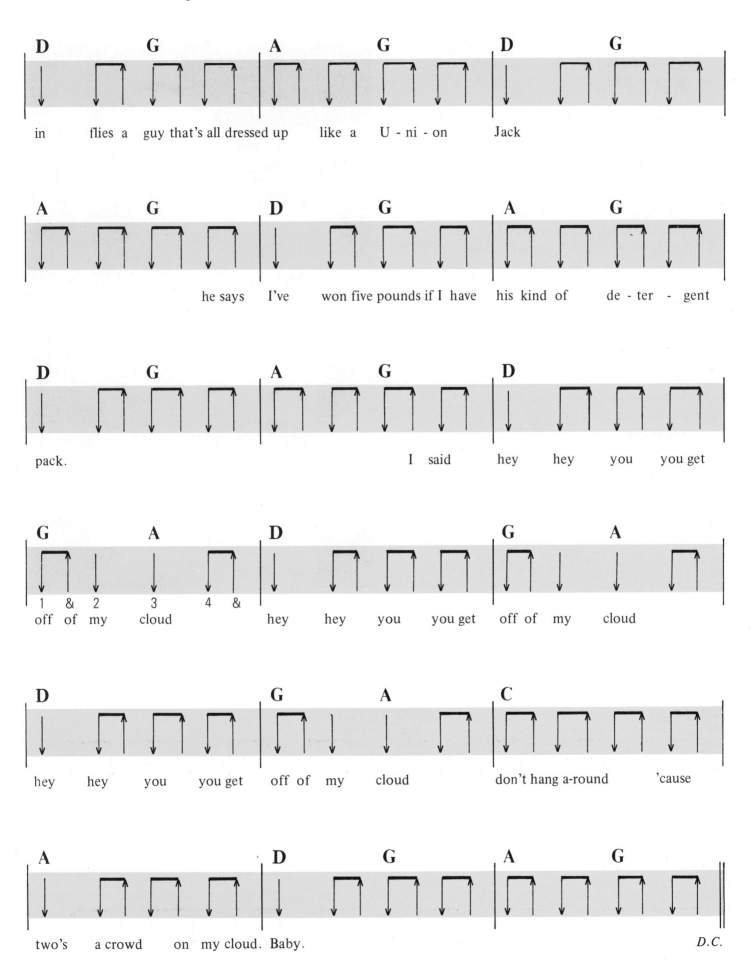

| D | G | A | G | D | G |
in flies a guy that's all dressed up like a U - ni - on Jack

| A | G | D | G | A | G |
he says I've won five pounds if I have his kind of de - ter - gent

| D | G | A | G | D |
pack. I said hey hey you you get

| G | A | D | G | A |
1 & 2 3 4 & hey hey you you get off of my cloud
off of my cloud

| D | G | A | C |
hey hey you you get off of my cloud don't hang a-round 'cause

| A | D | G | A | G |
two's a crowd on my cloud. Baby.

D.C.

N.B. The full lyric for each song can be found at the back of the book.

That'll Be The Day
Words & Music: Norman Petty, Buddy Holly, Jerry Allison

Again, the chords you have already learnt will see you through this famous rock 'n' roll standard. There are, however, some important new things to learn.

This song is played in the same swing-shuffle style which you learnt for 'Tom Hark' but there are a couple of important additions. First, look at the last bar of the verse. This very simple strum pattern is something you've heard hundreds of times on rock and pop records. Just tap your foot four times in the bar as usual but each time you tap your foot count 1,2,3 for each tap and strum as shown. Do you recognise the rhythm? Easy isn't it? Three notes played in the time of one are called triplets and are written .

This will be explained fully in a later book. For the moment, you need not concern yourself with this.

The only other thing you have to learn before you start to play is how to leave something out. Look at the last two bars of the chorus. Two bars from the end you will notice a sign saying 'let chord ring'. This means that you should strum the first beat of the bar only, but let the chord sound for the full four beats. At the start of the last bar there is a small sign that has not been mentioned before, known as a 'rest'. This, too, will be explained more fully in a later book. It means that you don't play on the '1' of the bar. Start on the '&' with an upstroke as shown, and you'll be ready for the rest of the bar. As always, you'll soon recognise the phrase.

CHORUS
Swing/Shuffle

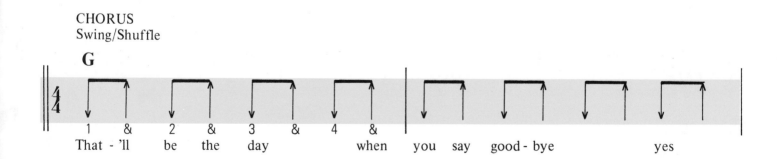

G

1 & 2 & 3 & 4 &
That - 'll be the day when you say good - bye yes

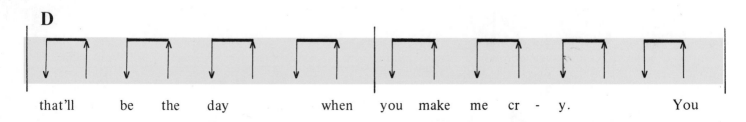

D

that'll be the day when you make me cr - y. You

That'll Be The Day Continued

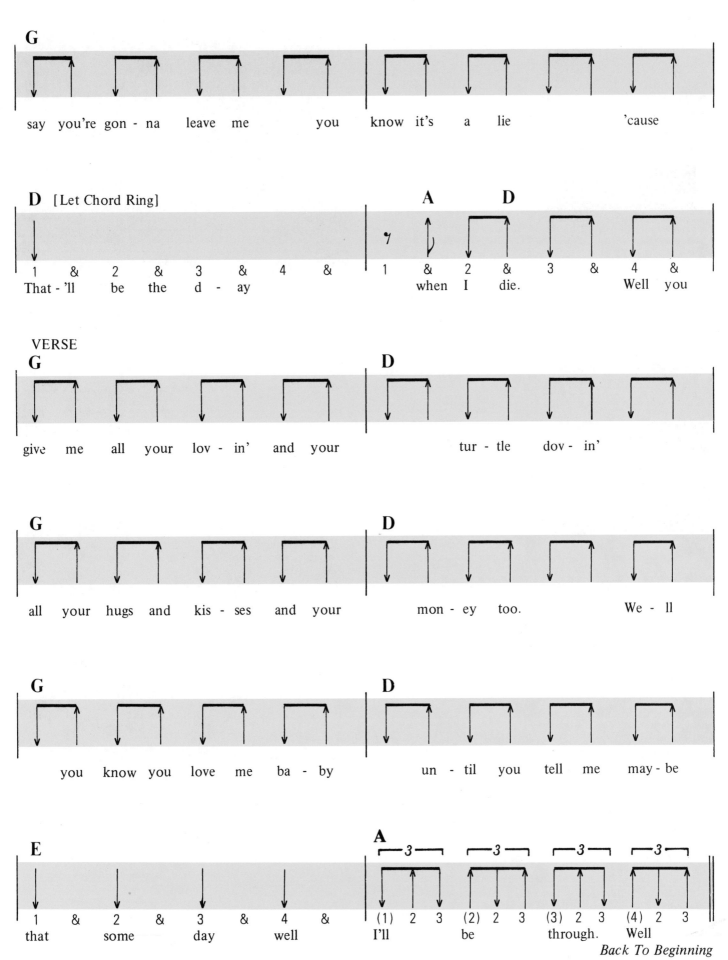

G

say you're gon - na leave me you   know it's a lie 'cause

D [Let Chord Ring]

1 & 2 & 3 & 4 &
That - 'll be the d - ay

A   **D**

1 & 2 & 3 & 4 &
when I die. Well you

VERSE
G

give me all your lov - in' and your

D

tur - tle dov - in'

G

all your hugs and kis - ses and your

D

mon - ey too. We - ll

G

you know you love me ba - by

D

un - til you tell me may - be

E

1 & 2 & 3 & 4 &
that some day well

A

(1) 2 3 (2) 2 3 (3) 2 3 (4) 2 3
I'll be through. Well

Back To Beginning

N.B. The full lyric for each song can be found at the back of the book.

© Copyright 1957 MPL Communications Inc.
Southern Music Publishing Co. Ltd., 8 Denmark Street,
London WC2.
All rights reserved. International copyright secured.

Black Magic Woman   Words & Music: Peter Green

The **D minor** Chord

The **Dm** Chord

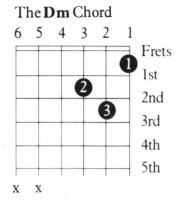

To play **D minor** place your 1st finger on the 1st fret of the 1st string and then locate the other positions.

The **A minor** Chord

The **A m** Chord

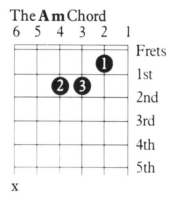

For **A minor** place your 1st finger on the 1st fret of the 2nd string and then locate the other positions. Practise changing between the two chords until you can do it clearly. Use a slow tempo to practise so that you don't have to stop for each change. Remember that playing evenly is the most important thing. You will notice that 'minor' chords have a sad sound and are often used by composers to give a melancholy feel to a song.

Finally, this little guitar figure is an important part of the song and occurs on the rest bar of each verse. So, for verse 1 you should start to play it as you sing the word 'me' at the beginning of the last bar. It is written out below in easy notation, with the appropriate excerpt from the lyric.

String	⌐3⌐		⌐4⌐		⌐5⌐			6	5
Fret	2	0	2	0	3	2	0	3	0

try'n to make a devil out of me

18

Black Magic Woman   Continued

STRAIGHT EIGHTS

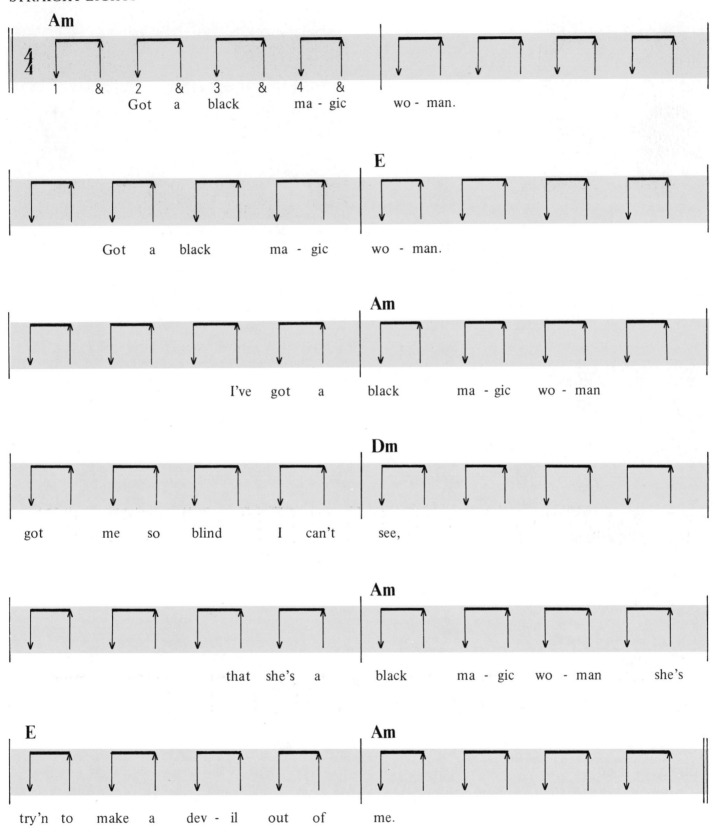

Am

1 & 2 & 3 & 4 & Got a black ma - gic wo - man.

Got a black ma - gic wo - man. E

I've got a black ma - gic wo - man Am

got me so blind I can't see, Dm

that she's a black ma - gic wo - man she's Am

try'n to make a dev - il out of me. Am / E

N.B. The full lyric for each song can be found at the back of the book.

Stand By Me

Words & Music: Ben E. King, Jerry Lieber and Mike Stoller

The **E minor** Chord

The **E m** Chord

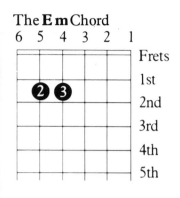

You learnt your first minor chords for the last song. Well, here's another one. It's called **E minor** and we're going to use it in this next song which, incidentally, has been a hit for several artists, including an outstanding version by John Lennon on his 'Rock 'n' Roll' album.

First, let's examine the new chord. You'll notice it's exactly the same as the **E** chord you have already learnt but without the first finger on the third string. There is an important 'musical reason' why this is so and we will talk about that in later books.

Up to now we have had a maximum of two strums per tap of the foot and we have been counting 1 & 2 & etc. for each tap. If you look at the first beat of each bar you will see there is an extra strum between the '&' sign and the '2'. Count this extra strum as an 'a'.

To recap, the rhythm of each bar is counted as 1 & a 2 & 3 & 4 &. Remember, you must arrive at the '2' on the second foot tap so you have to squeeze the 'a' strum in between the '&' and the '2'.

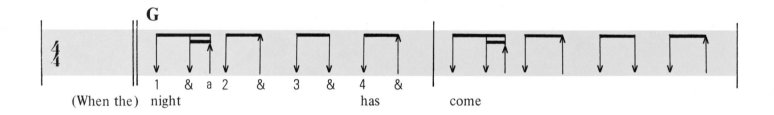

(When the) night   has   come

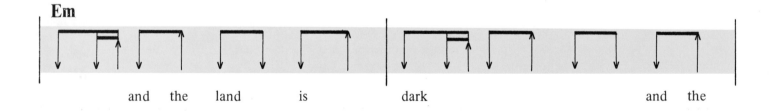

and the land is   dark   and the

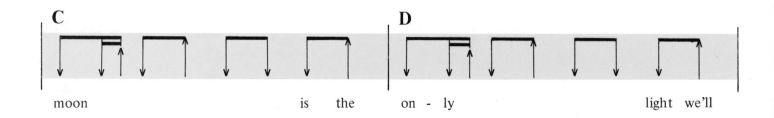

moon   is the   on-ly   light we'll

Stand By Me Continued

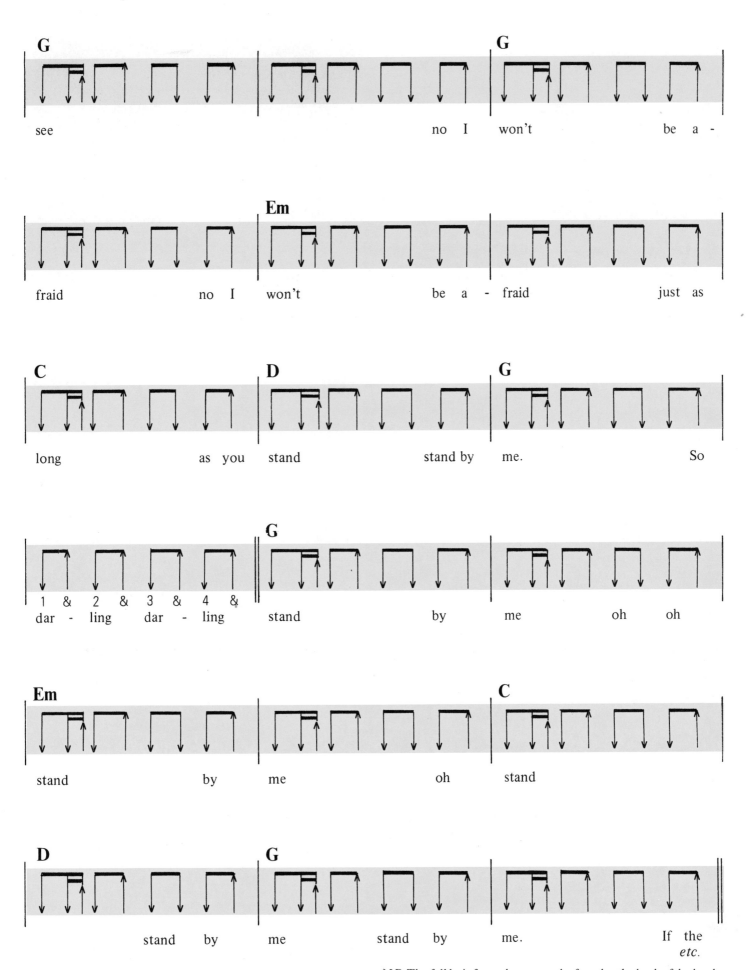

G see | no I won't | **G** be a -

G fraid | **Em** no I won't be a - fraid | just as

C long as you | **D** stand stand by | **G** me. So

1 & 2 & 3 & 4 & dar - ling dar - ling | **G** stand by | me oh oh

Em stand by | me | **C** oh stand

D stand by | **G** me stand by | me. If the

etc.

© Copyright 1961 Trio Music Co. Ltd., USA.
Trio Music Ltd., 14 New Burlington Street,
London W1 for the British Commonwealth (exc.
Canada and Australasia), South Africa, Eire and Israel.
All rights reserved. International copyright secured.

N.B. The full lyric for each song can be found at the back of the book.

Paint It Black

Words & Music: Mick Jagger & Keith Richard

The **E seventh** Chord

The **E 7** Chord

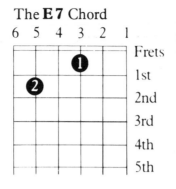

This new chord is very easy to play because you have already learnt the **E** chord for 'Summertime Blues'. All you have to do is place your fingers in the same position as for the **E** chord and simply remove your 3rd finger from the fretboard, and allow the open 4th (or D) string to sound. Remember to keep your fingers as near vertical to the fretboard as possible. You may find that if you are not careful the pad of your 2nd finger will interfere with the clear ringing of the open 4th string.

You will notice that the **E 7** chord has an 'expectant' sound, and goes well when played before **A** or **A minor.** It has been used by many artists as a lead-in chord to a song. Just strum **E 7** once letting it ring and you will understand what is meant.

STRAIGHT EIGHTS

Am

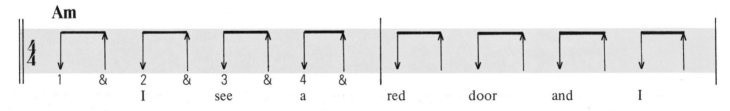

1 & 2 & 3 & 4 &
I see a red door and I

E7

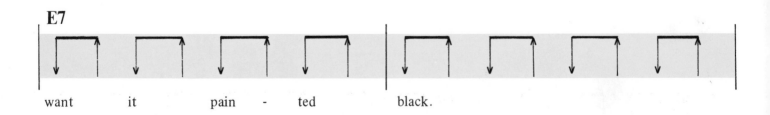

want it pain - ted black.

22

Paint It Black Continued

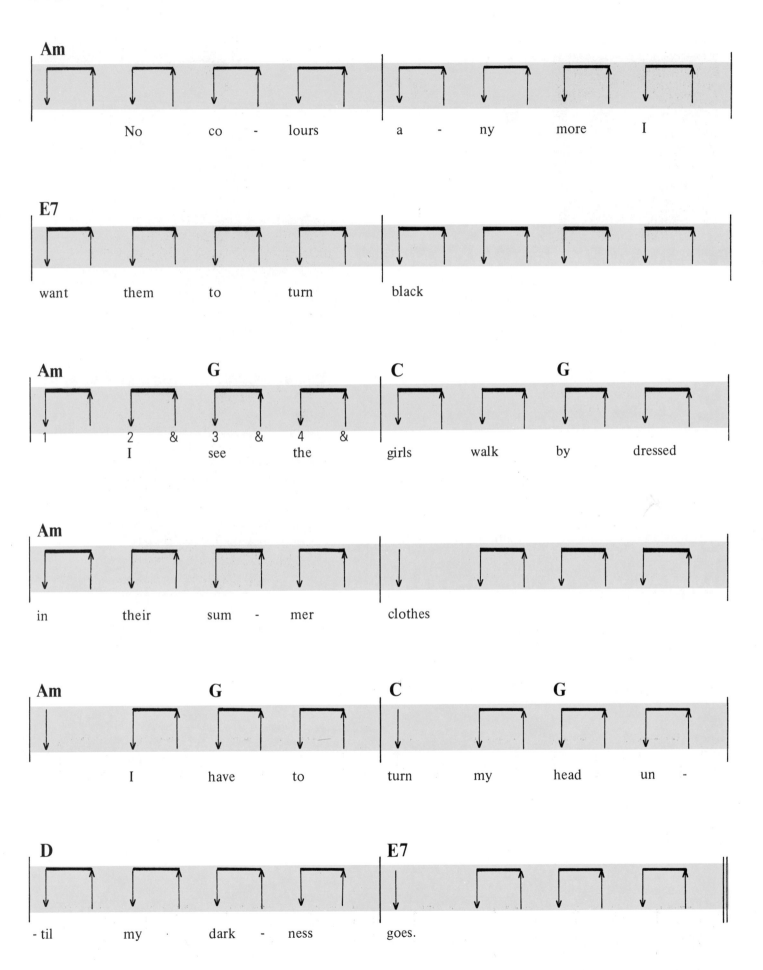

Am

No co - lours a - ny more I

E7

want them to turn black

Am **G** **C** **G**

1 2 & 3 & 4 & girls walk by dressed
I see the

Am

in their sum - mer clothes

Am **G** **C** **G**

I have to turn my head un -

D **E7**

- til my dark - ness goes.

N.B. The full lyric for each song can be found at the back of the book.

© Copyright 1966 ABKCO Music Inc., USA.
Westminster Music Ltd, 19/20 Poland Street,
London W1.
All rights reserved. International copyright secured.

Ob-La-Di Words & Music: John Lennon and Paul McCartney

The **G seventh** Chord

The **G 7** Chord

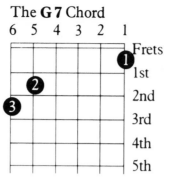

This big hit by Lennon and McCartney introduces another 7th chord. This is **G 7**. Unfortunately, it is not quite as easy to change **G** into **G 7** as it was to change **E** into **E 7** but by now you should not have any trouble with it.

What you must do is completely change the fingering between the two chords. Study the chord box for **G 7** and the earlier chord box for **G**, and you'll see what is meant.

Practise the change between these two chords and then we will talk about the strumming.

The pattern here is the 'straight eight' feel with which you should be familiar by now. The only difference is that you accent what is called the 'off beat'. The 'off beat' is the strum you play on each count of '&'.

You will recognise the rhythm. It is used all the time in reggae music.

STRAIGHT EIGHTS

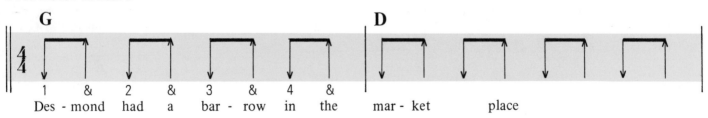

G								D
1	&	2	&	3	&	4	&	
Des - mond	had	a	bar - row	in	the			mar - ket place

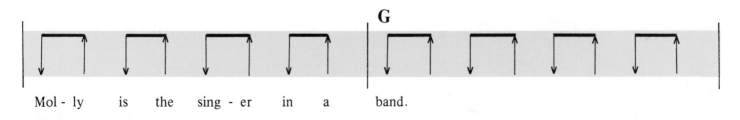

Mol - ly   is   the   sing - er   in   a   band.

24

Ob-La-Di, Ob-La-Da Continued

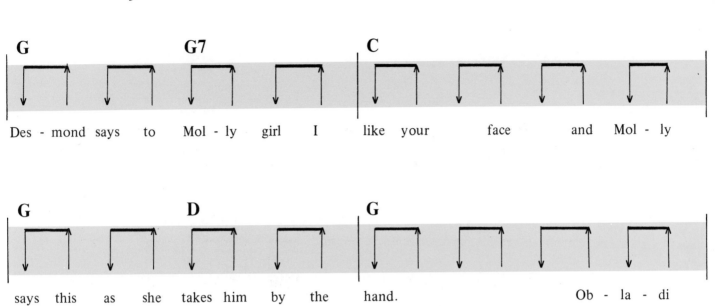

G　　　　　　　G7　　　　　　　　　　　C

Des - mond says to Mol - ly girl I　like your face and Mol - ly

G　　　　　　　D　　　　　　　　　　　G

says this as she takes him by the hand.　　　Ob - la - di

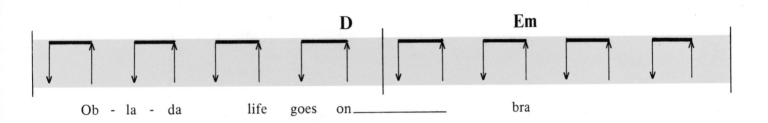

　　　　　　　　　　　　D　　　　　　Em

Ob - la - da life goes on＿＿＿＿＿＿ bra

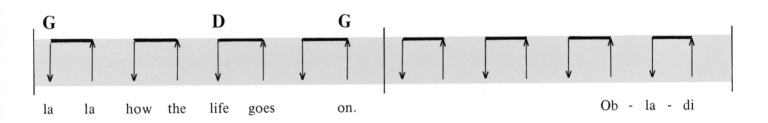

G　　　　　　D　　G

la la how the life goes on.　　　　Ob - la - di

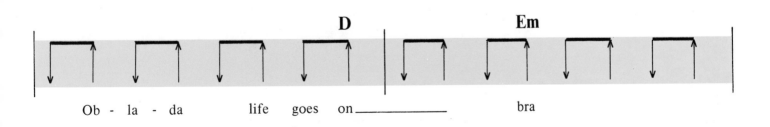

　　　　　　　　　　　D　　　　　Em

Ob - la - da life goes on＿＿＿＿＿＿ bra

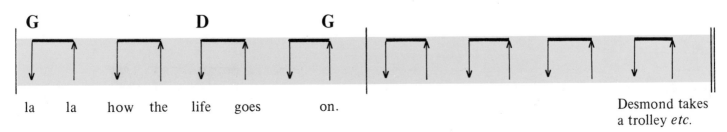

G　　　　　D　　G

la la how the life goes on.　　　　Desmond takes
a trolley *etc.*

N.B. The full lyric for each song can be found at the back of the book.

Karma Chameleon

Words & Music: O'Dowd, Moss, Hay, Craig and Pickett

The strum pattern is familiar and you know all the chords so enjoy yourself with this famous song.

STRAIGHT EIGHTS

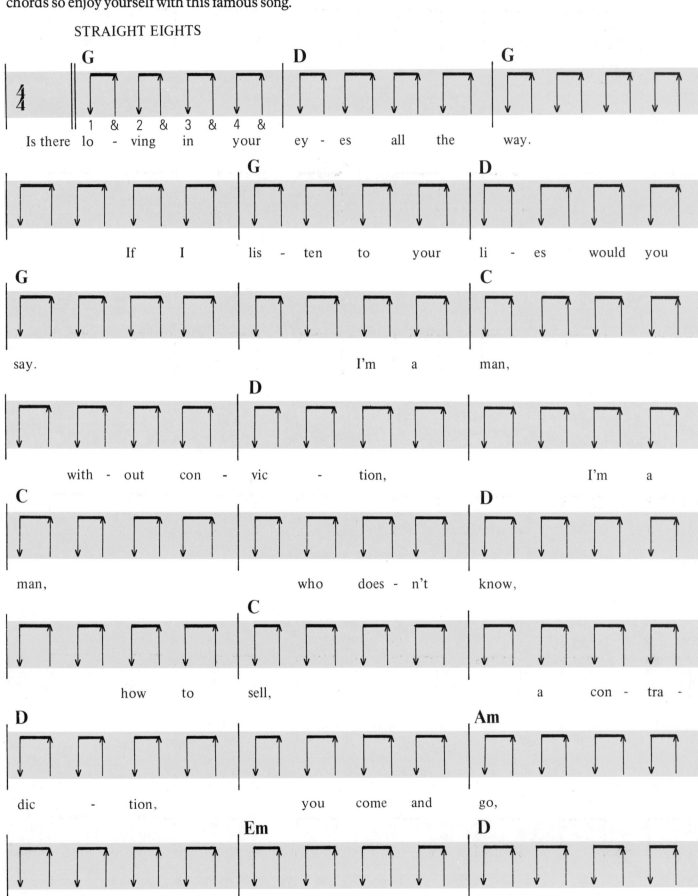

G   D   G

1 & 2 & 3 & 4 &

Is there lo - ving in your ey - es all the way.

G   D

If I lis - ten to your li - es would you

G   C

say.   I'm a man,

D

with - out con - vic - tion, I'm a

C   D

man, who does - n't know,

C

how to sell, a con - tra -

D   Am

dic - tion, you come and go,

Em   D

you come and go.

Karma Chameleon Continued

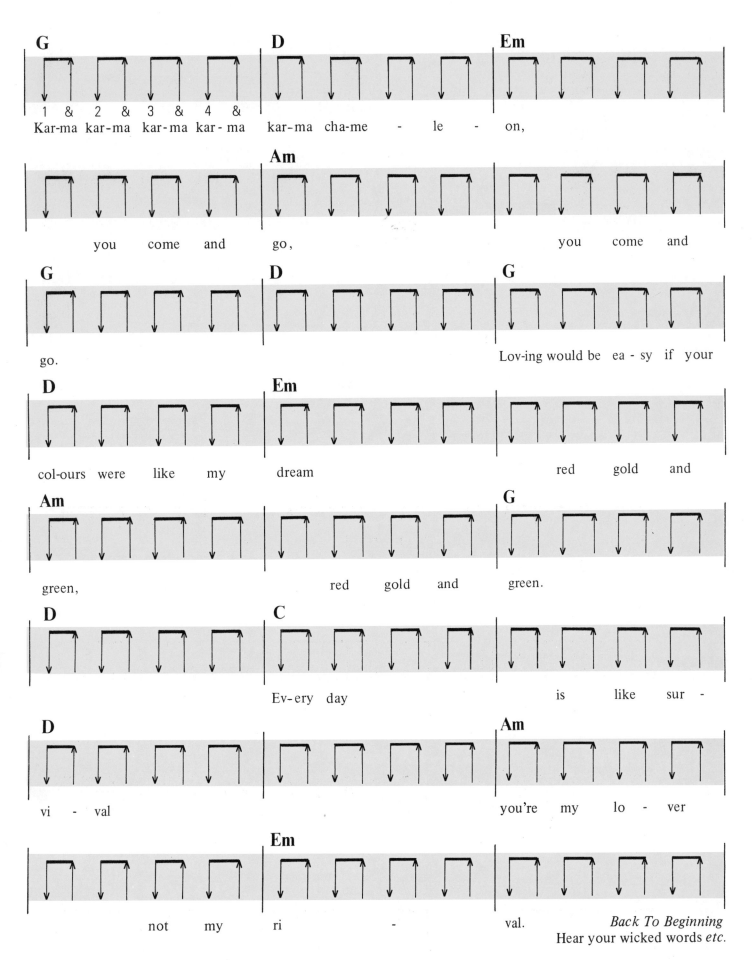

G | **D** | **Em**
1 & 2 & 3 & 4 &
Kar-ma kar-ma kar-ma kar-ma · kar-ma cha-me - le - on,

Am
you come and · go, · you come and

G | **D** | **G**
go. · Lov-ing would be ea - sy if your

D | **Em**
col-ours were like my · dream · red gold and

Am | **G**
green, · red gold and · green.

D | **C**
Ev-ery day · is like sur -

D | **Am**
vi - val · you're my lo - ver

Em
not my ri - val. *Back To Beginning*
Hear your wicked words *etc*.

© Copyright 1983 Virgin Music (Publishers) Ltd.,
95/99 Ladbroke Grove, London W11. Pendulum
Music Ltd/Warner Bros Music Ltd., 17 Berners Street,
London.
All rights reserved. International copyright secured.

N.B. The full lyric for each song can be found at the back of the book.

Livin' On A Prayer
Words & Music: John Bon Jovi, Richie Sambora & Desmond Child

The **E minor 7** Chord

The **Em7** Chord

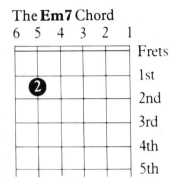

This massive hit by Bon Jovi introduces a subtle variation on the Em chord you have already learnt. Play the Em chord - which should be familiar by now - and simply remove your third finger. You should find you are making the shape shown above. Notice the subtle difference between Em and Em7.

Later you will learn how to turn all your minors into minor sevenths, but for now Em7 is all you need.

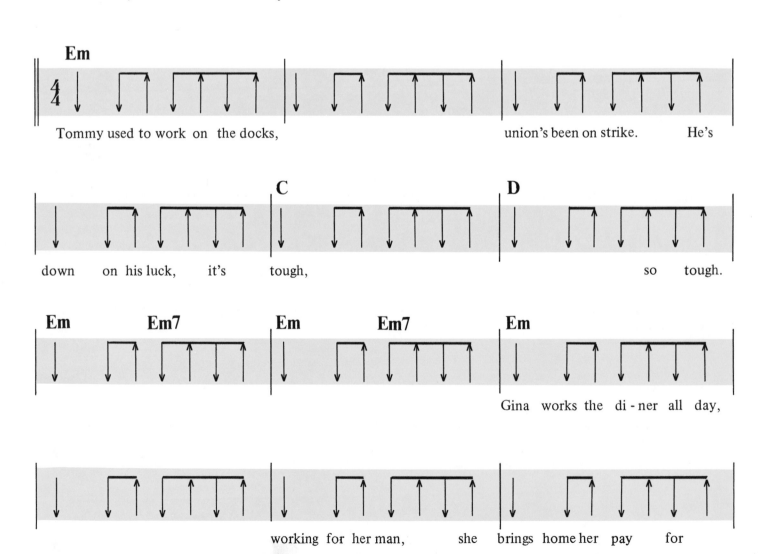

Em

Tommy used to work on the docks, union's been on strike. He's

down on his luck, it's **C** tough, **D** so tough.

Em   **Em7**   **Em**   **Em7**   **Em**

Gina works the di-ner all day,

working for her man, she brings home her pay for

28

Livin' On A Prayer _{Continued}

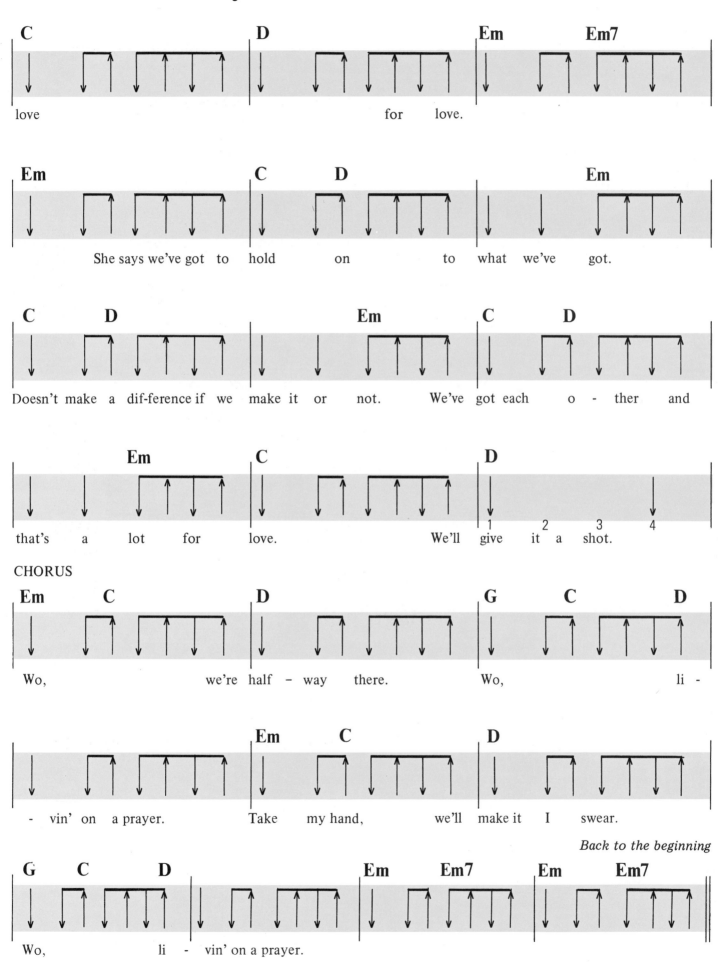

C love

D for love.

Em **Em7**

Em She says we've got to **C** **D** hold on to what we've **Em** got.

C **D** Doesn't make a dif-ference if we **Em** make it or not. We've **C** **D** got each o - ther and

Em that's a lot for **C** love. We'll **D** give it a shot.
1 2 3 4

CHORUS

Em Wo, **C** we're **D** half – way there. **G** Wo, **C** **D** li -

Em - vin' on a prayer. **C** Take my hand, **D** we'll make it I swear.

Back to the beginning

G Wo, **C** li - **D** vin' on a prayer. **Em** **Em7** **Em** **Em7**

© Copyright 1986 Bon Jovi Publishing/SBK Songs International/Desmobile Music Company Polygram Music Publishing Incorporated. Polygram Music Publishing Limited, Chancellors House, Chancellors Road, London W6 (66 2/3%) - EMI Songs Limited, 127 Charing Cross Road, London WC2 (33 1/3%). All Rights Reserved. International Copyright Secured.

N.B. The full lyric for each song can be found at the back of the book.

My Own Way   Words & Music: Duran Duran

This big hit by Duran Duran doesn't introduce anything new. Apart from being a great song it uses seven chords you already know and makes a great practice piece. Remember, one of the secrets of being a good guitar player is being able to change smoothly from one chord to another and here's a great chance to practise this. Watch the rhythm pattern in the last eight bars. The rest sign 𝄾 which was introduced in 'That'll Be The Day' means you don't play anything on that beat.

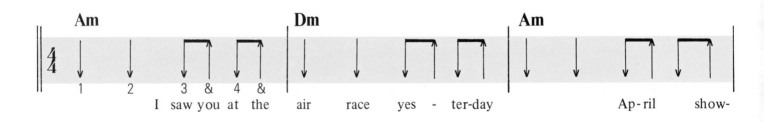

Am   Dm   Am

1   2   3 & 4 &   I saw you at the   air race yes - ter-day   Ap - ril   show-

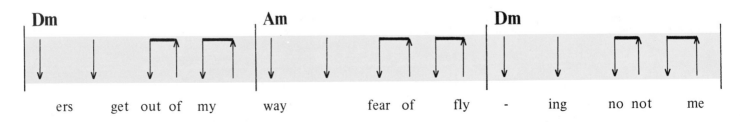

Dm   Am   Dm

ers   get out of my   way   fear of fly - ing   no not me

My Own Way   Continued

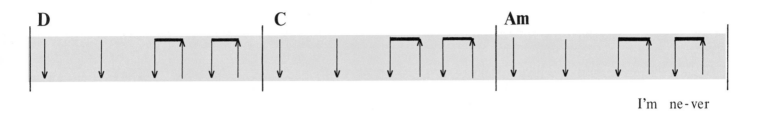

D | C | Am

I'm ne-ver

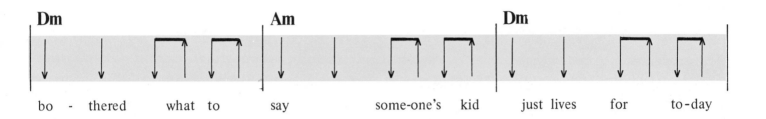

Dm | Am | Dm

bo - thered   what to   say   some-one's kid   just lives   for   to-day

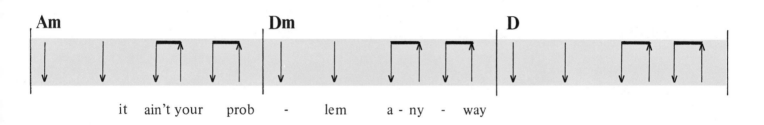

Am | Dm | D

it   ain't your   prob - lem   a - ny - way

CHORUS

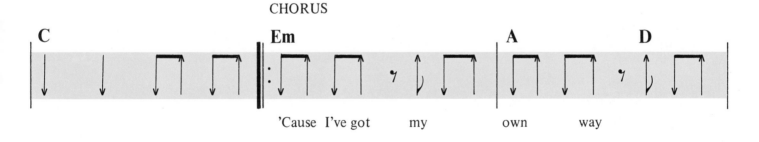

C | Em | A   D

'Cause I've got   my   own   way

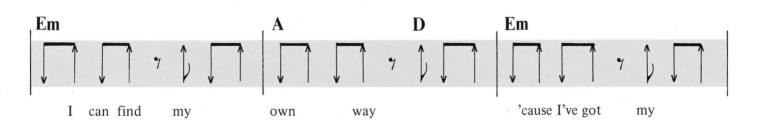

Em | A   D | Em

I can find   my   own   way   'cause I've got   my

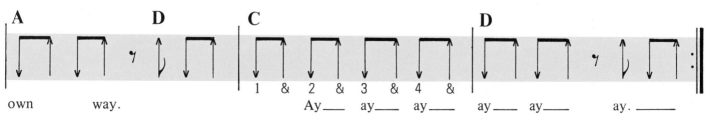

A   D | C | D

own   way.   1 & 2 & 3 & 4 &   Ay___ ay___ ay___   ay___ ay___   ay. ___

Repeat
Last 8 Bars.

N.B. The full lyric for each song can be found at the back of the book.

Sailing

Words & Music: Gavin Sutherland

For Rod Stewart's big hit 'Sailing', a style of playing is introduced which allows you to add a bass line to your strumming. The letters you see incorporated with the strum marks refer to single notes and you are going to learn where to find them on the guitar. The G is played with the finger stopping the 3rd fret on the 6th string (you'll find your finger is already there to play the G chord), the F$\sharp$ is 6th string 2nd fret, the E is the open 6th string, A is open A and the C is found 3rd fret 5th string.

Simply play the note where shown and strum the appropriate chord. You'll find you're playing a very nice bass line to go with this great hit.

Sailing Continued

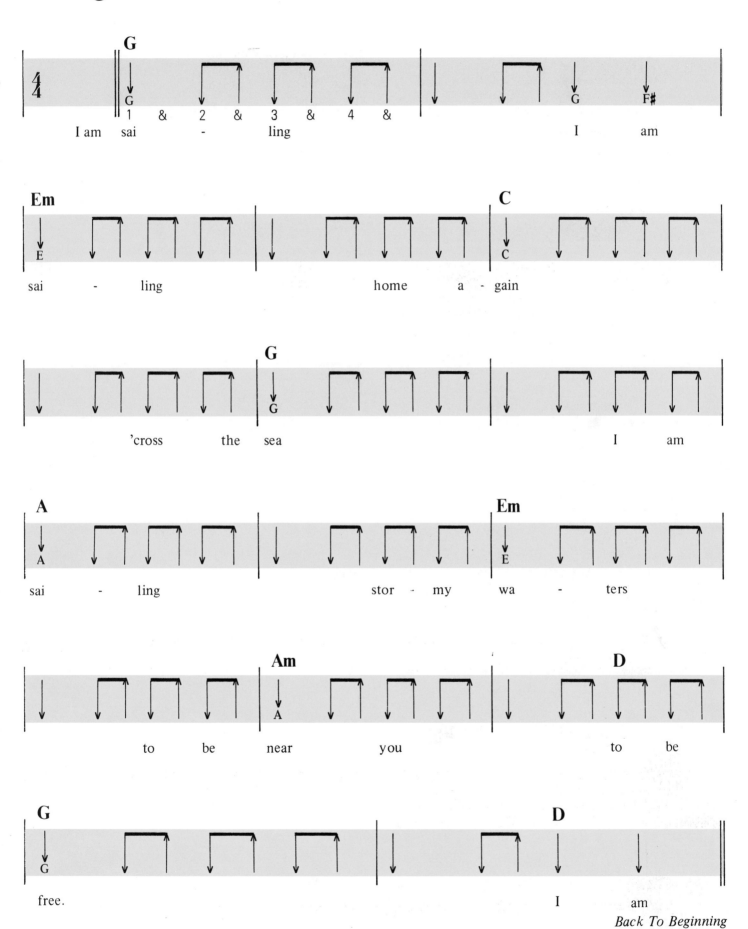

I am sai - ling   I am
sai - ling   home a - gain
'cross the sea   I am
sai - ling   stor - my wa - ters
to be near you   to be
free.   I am

Back To Beginning

N.B. The full lyric for each song can be found at the back of the book.

© Copyright 1972 by Island Music Ltd, 22 St. Peter's Square, London W 6.
All rights reserved. International copyright secured.

One More Night   Words & Music: Phil Collins

The B minor Chord

The Bm Chord

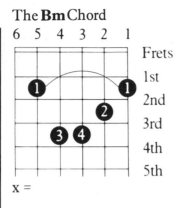

x =

This fantastic hit by Phil Collins introduces a very important chord shape. All the chords you have previously learnt have used some open strings, whereas with this all the strings you strum are being 'stopped' with your fingers. This means that you can move the shape up and down the neck to make different chords, in this case minors. For instance, if you move your hand up one fret from the position shown, you will be playing **Cm**, up two frets and you're playing **C♯m**. We won't dwell on this for now, but isn't it great to know that in one go you've learnt possibly 10 minor chords?

For the purpose of this book, the timing of the middle section has been very slightly altered to make it easier to play.

STRAIGHT EIGHTS

Repeat Two Bars

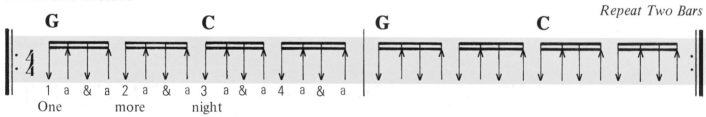

1 a & a 2 a & a 3 a & a 4 a & a
One   more   night

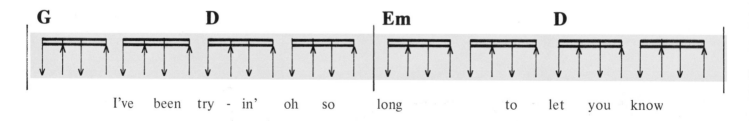

I've   been   try - in'   oh   so   long   to   let   you   know

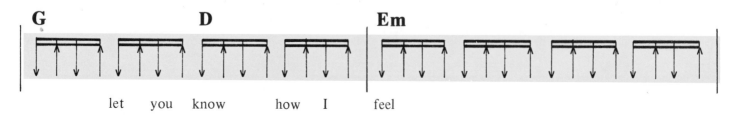

let   you   know   how   I   feel

34

One More Night   Continued

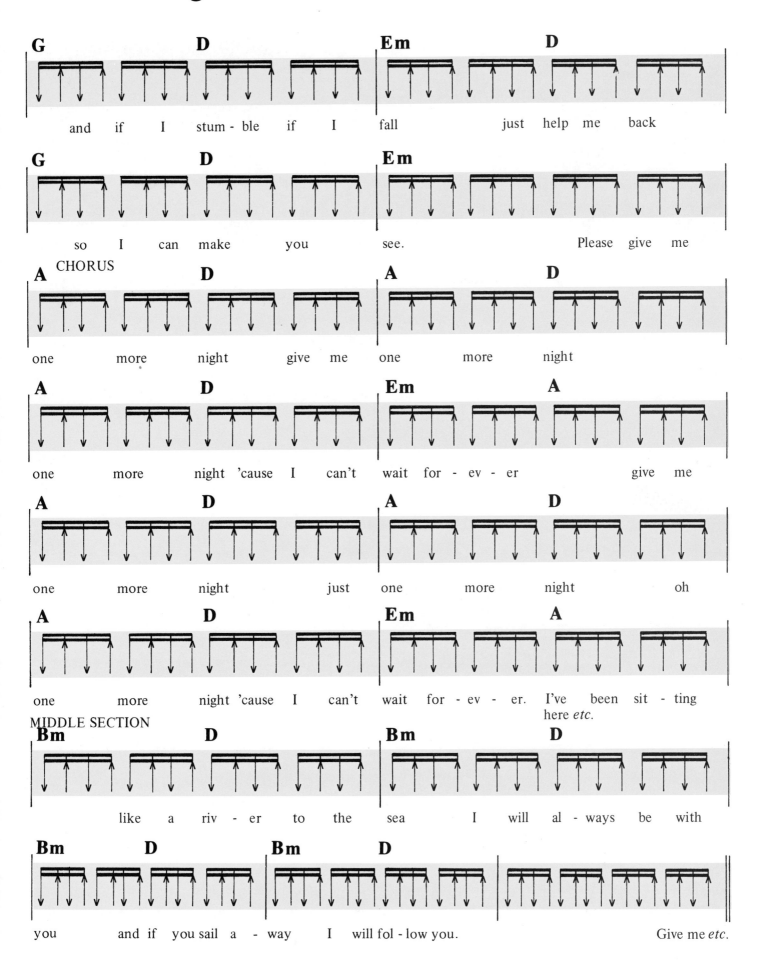

G   **D**   **Em**   **D**

and if I stum-ble if I fall   just help me back

G   **D**   **Em**

so I can make you see.   Please give me

A CHORUS   **D**   **A**   **D**

one more night give me one more night

A   **D**   **Em**   **A**

one more night 'cause I can't wait for - ev - er give me

A   **D**   **A**   **D**

one more night just one more night oh

A   **D**   **Em**   **A**

one more night 'cause I can't wait for - ev - er. I've been sit - ting here *etc*.

MIDDLE SECTION

Bm   **D**   **Bm**   **D**

like a riv - er to the sea I will al - ways be with

Bm   **D**   **Bm**   **D**

you and if you sail a - way I will fol - low you. Give me *etc*.

Words & Music: Phil Collins

N.B. The full lyric for each song can be found at the back of the book.

© Copyright 1984 Phil Collins Ltd/Hit & Run Music (Publishing) Ltd., 81-83 Walton Street, London SW3. All rights reserved. International copyright secured.

Dance Away The Heartaches
Words & Music: Bryan Ferry

The **F♯ minor** Chord

The **F♯m** Chord

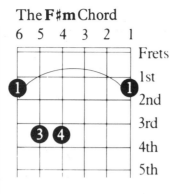

Well, you need only one more chord to play along with Bryan Ferry and 'Dance Away The Heartaches'. This shape is another moveable one, like the **Bm** in the previous piece. In the position shown above it is **F♯ minor.** Move it up one fret and it becomes **G minor,** down a fret it becomes **F minor.**

Try putting your first finger across the six strings and getting each note to sound clearly before adding your third and fourth fingers. You'll find it's easier that way.

Well folks, that's it. Keep practising. You are now ready for Book 2. There's lots more exciting things to come.

G

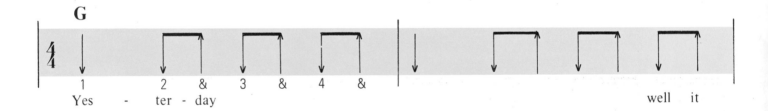

Yes - ter - day   well it

Em

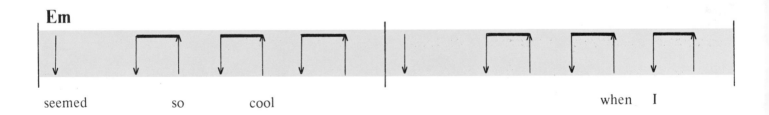

seemed   so   cool   when I

C   **D**   **C**

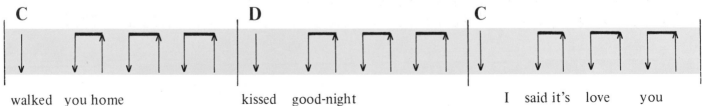

walked you home   kissed good-night   I said it's love you

36

Dance Away The Heartaches Continued

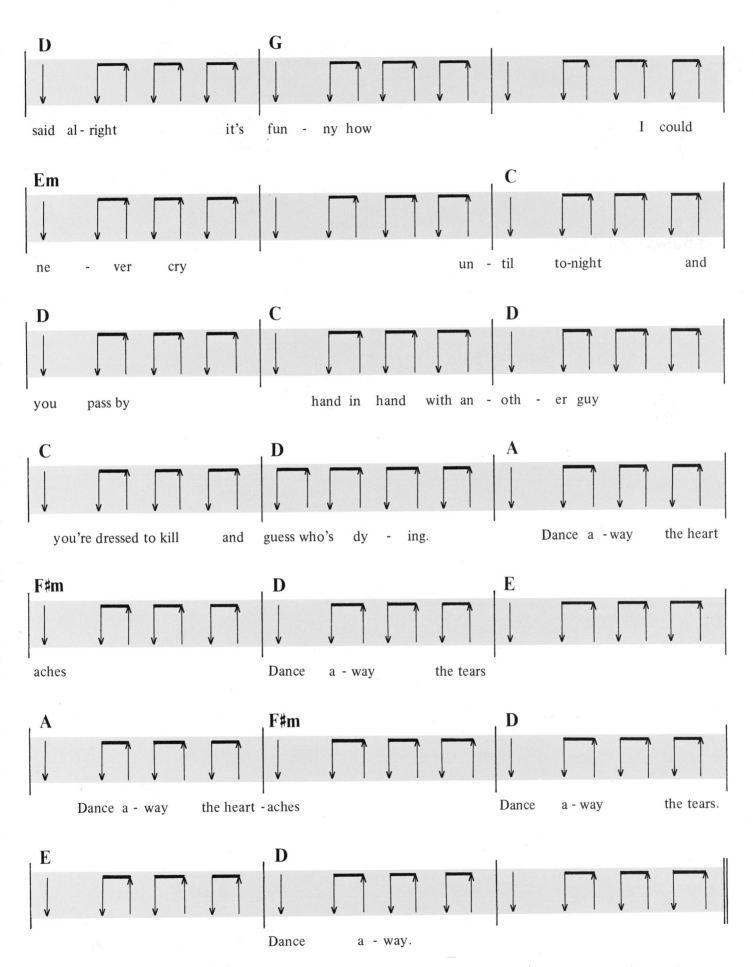

D said al - right **G** it's fun - ny how I could

Em ne - ver cry **C** un - til to-night and

D you pass by **C** hand in hand with an - oth - er guy **D**

C you're dressed to kill and **D** guess who's dy - ing. **A** Dance a - way the heart

F♯m aches **D** Dance a - way the tears **E**

A Dance a - way the heart - aches **F♯m** Dance a - way the tears. **D**

E **D** Dance a - way.

Words & Music: Bryan Ferry

© Copyright 1979 E.G. Music Ltd., 63a Kings Road, London SW 3.
All rights reserved. International copyright secured.

N.B. The full lyric for each song can be found at the back of the book.

Mull Of Kintyre

Mull of Kintyre,
Oh mist rolling in from the sea,
My desire is always to be here,
Oh Mull of Kintyre.

Far have I travelled and much have I seen,
Dark distant mountains with valleys of green,
Past painted deserts, the sunset's on fire,
As he carries me home to the Mull of Kintyre.

Mull of Kintyre,
Oh mist rolling in from the sea,
My desire is always to be here,
Oh Mull of Kintyre.

Smiles in the sunshine and tears in the rain,
Still take me back where my mem'ries remain.
Flickering embers grow higher and high'r
As they carry me back to the Mull of Kintyre.

Mull of Kintyre,
Oh mist rolling in from the sea,
My desire is always to be here,
Oh Mull of Kintyre.

Sweep through the heather like deer in the glen,
Carry me back to the days I knew then.
Nights when we sang like a heavenly choir
Of the life and the times of the Mull of Kintyre.

Mull of Kintyre.
Mull of Kintyre.

Tom Hark

Does anybody know how long to World War III?
I want to know I've got to book my holiday.
They want me in the army, but I just can't go,
I'm far too busy list'ning to the radio.
Chorus:
The whole thing's daft, I don't know why,
You'll have to laugh or else you'll cry.
You'll have to live or else you'll die
You'll have to laugh or else you'll cry.

My friends say that we're heading for a grotty time.
It's just a load of slapstick in a pantomime.
We're heading for a disaster, well, I just don't care.
Shut your eyes and count to ten, you won't be there.

Chorus.

Summertime Blues

Well I'm a-gonna raise a fuss, I'm a-gonna raise a holler,
About a workin' all summer just to try to earn a dollar,
Ev'ry time I call my Baby, try to get a date,
My boss says, "No dice, Son, you gotta work late",
Sometimes I wonder what I'm a-gonna do,
But there ain't no cure for the Summertime Blues.

A well my Mom 'n' Papa told me, "Son, you gotta make
    some money,
If you want-ta use the car to go a ridin' next Sunday",
Well, I didn't go to work, told the boss I was sick,
"Now you can't use the car 'cause you didn't work a lick."
Sometimes I wonder what I'm a-gonna do,
But there ain't no cure for the Summertime Blues.

I'm gonna take two weeks gonna have a fine vacation,
I'm gonna take my problem to the United Nations!
Well, I called my Congressman and he said (quote)
"I'd like to help you, Son, but you're too young to vote."
Sometimes I wonder what I'm a-gonna do.
But there ain't no cure for the Summertime Blues.

Hello, I Love You

Hello, I love you,
Won't you tell me your name?
Hello, I love you,
Let me jump in your game.
Hello, I love you,
Won't you tell me your name?
Hello, I love you,
Let me jump in your game.

She's walkin' down the street,
Blind to ev'ry eye she meets,
Do you think you'll be the guy
To make the queen of the angels sigh?

Hello, I love you,
Won't you tell me your name?
Hello, I love you,
Let me jump in your game.
Hello, I love you,
Won't you tell me your name?
Hello, I love you,
Let me jump in your game.

She holds her head so high,
Like a statue in the sky.
Her arms are wicked and her legs are long,
When she moves, my brain screams out this song.

Sidewalk crouches at her feet
Like a dog that begs for something sweet.
Do you hope to make her see, you fool?
Do you hope to pluck this dusky jewel?

Hello, Hello, Hello, Hello.

Get Off Of My Cloud

I live in an apartment on the ninety-ninth floor of my
    block,
And I sit at home lookin' out the window imagining the
    world has stopped
Then in flies a guy that's all dressed up like a Union
    Jack,
He says I've won five pounds if I have his kind of
    detergent pack.
Chorus:
I said Hey (Hey) you (You) Get off of my cloud!
Hey (Hey) you (You) Get off of my cloud!
Hey (Hey) you (You) Get off of my cloud!
Don't hang around, 'cause two's a crowd on my cloud
    baby.

The telephone is ringin' I say "Hi it's me Who's there on
    the line?"
A voice says, "Hi hullo. How are you?" Well I guess I'm
    doing fine
He says, "It's three a.m. and there's too much noise
Don't you people ever want to go to bed?
Just 'cause you feel so good, do you have to drive me out
    of my head?

Chorus.

I was sick and tired, fed up with this and decided to take
    a drive down town.
It was so very quiet and peaceful. There was nobody, not
    a soul around.
I laid myself out I was so tired and I started to dream.
In the mornin' the parkin' tickets were just like flags
    stuck on my windscreen.

Chorus.

That'll Be The Day

Well, you give me all your lovin' and your turtle dovin',
All your hugs and kisses and your money too;
Well, you know you love me, baby,
Until you tell me, maybe, that some day, well, I'll be
    through!
Chorus:
Well, that'll be the day, when you say goodbye,
Yes, that'll be the day, when you make me cry,
You say you're gonna leave, you know it's a lie,
'Cause that'll be the day when I die.

When Cupid shot his dart, he shot it at your heart,
So if we ever part and I leave you,
You say you told me and you told me boldly,
That some day, well, I'll be through.

Chorus.

Black Magic Woman

Got a black magic woman.
Got a black magic woman,
I've got a black magic woman.
Got me so blind I can't see that she's a black magic
    woman,
She's try'n to make a devil out of me.

Turn your back on me baby,
Turn your back on me baby,
Yes don't turn your back on me baby.
Stop messin' round with your tricks,
Don't turn your back on me, baby, you just might pick up
    my magic sticks.

Got your spell on me baby,
Got your spell on me baby,
Yes you got your spell on me baby, turning my heart into
    stone.
I need you so bad, magic woman, I can't leave you alone.

Stand By Me

When the night has come and the land is dark,
And the moon is the only light we'll see
No I won't be afraid, no I won't be afraid
Just as long as you stand, stand by me.

So, darling, darling stand by me.
Oh, oh, stand by me, oh, stand, stand by me, stand by me.

If the sea that we look upon should tumble and fall,
Or the mountain should crumble in the sea,
I won't cry, I won't cry, no I won't shed a tear
Just as long as you stand, stand by me.

So darling, darling stand by me.
Oh, stand by me, oh, stand, stand by me, stand by me.

Paint It Black

I see a red door and I want it painted black,
No colours any more I want them to turn black.
I see the girls walk by dressed in their summer clothes.
I have to turn my head until my darkness goes.

I see a line of cars and they're all painted black,
With flowers and my love both never to come back,
I see people turn their heads and quickly look away,
Like a new born baby it just happens ev'ry day.

I look inside myself and see my heart is black,
I see my red door and I want it painted black,
Maybe then I'll fade away and not have to face the facts,
It's not easy facing up when your whole world is black.

No more will my green sea go turn a deeper blue,
I could not foresee this thing happening to you,
If I look hard enough into the setting sun,
My love will laugh with me before the morning comes.

I see a red door and I want it painted black,
No colours any more I want them to turn black,
I see the girls walk by dressed in their summer clothes,
I have to turn my head until my darkness goes.

Ob-La-Di Ob-La-Da

Desmond had a barrow in the market place,
Molly is the singer in a band.
Desmond says to Molly, girl I like your face
And Molly says this as she takes him by the hand.
Ob-la-di, ob-la-da, life goes on bra.
La la how the life goes on.
Ob-la-di, ob-la-da, life goes on bra.
La la how the life goes on.

Desmond takes a trolley to the jeweller's store,
Buys a twenty carat golden ring,
Takes it back to Molly, waiting at the door
And as he gives it to her she begins to sing.
Ob-la-di, ob-la-da, life goes on bra.
La la how the life goes on.
Ob-la-di, ob-la-da, life goes on bra.
La la how the life goes on.

In a couple of years they have built a home sweet home
With a couple of kids running in the yard of Desmond
    and Molly Jones.

Happy ever after in the market place,
Desmond lets the children lend a hand.
Molly stays at home and does her pretty face
And in the evening she still sings it with the band.
Ob-la-di, ob-la-da, life goes on bra.
La la how the life goes on.
Ob-la-di, ob-la-da, life goes on bra.
La la how the life goes on.

Karma Chameleon

Is there loving in your eyes all the way?
If I listen to your lies would you say
I'm a man, without conviction?
I'm a man who doesn't know
How to sell a contradiction,
You come and go you come and go.

Karma karma karma karma karma chameleon
You come and go you come and go
Loving would be easy if your colours were like my dream
Red gold and green, red gold and green.

Hear your wicked words every day
And you used to be so sweet. I heard you say
That my love was an addiction.
When we cling our love is strong,
When you go you're gone forever,
You string along, you string along.

Karma karma karma karma karma chameleon
You come and go you come and go
Loving would be easy if your colours were like my dream
Red gold and green, red gold and green.

Every day is like survival
You're my lover not my rival.

Livin' On A Prayer

Tommy used to work on the docks,
Union's been on strike.
He's down on his luck,
It's tough, so tough.

Gina works the diner all day,
Working for her man.
She brings home her pay,
For love, for love.

She says we've got to
Hold on to what we've got.
Doesn't make a difference
If we make it or not.
We've got each other
And that's a lot for love.
We'll give it a shot.

Chorus.

Wo, we're halfway there.
Wo, livin' on a prayer.
Take my hand.
We'll make it I swear.
Wo, livin' on a prayer.

Tommy's got his six string in hock,
Now he's holding in
What he used to make it talk.
So tough, it's tough.

Gina dreams of running away;
When she cries in the night,
Tommy whispers: baby it's O.K.
Some day.

We've got to hold on
To what we've got.
Doesn't make a difference
If we make it or not.
We've got each other
And that's a lot for love.
We'll give it a shot.

Chorus.

Oh! we've got to hold on
Ready or not.
You live for the fight
When it's all that you've got.

My Own Way

I saw you at the air race yesterday
April showers get out of my way.
Fear of flying? No not me.
I'm never bothered what to say.
Someone's kid just lives for today.
It ain't your problem anyway.
Chorus:
'Cause I've got my own way.
I can find my own way.
'Cause I've got my own way,
Ay ay ay ay ay ay
'Cause I've got my own way.
I can find my own way
Ay ay ay ay ay ay
Number one.

Public figure what a pain
Just puts another rattle in your brain.
Take another green but it's not the same.
So now you're on the sand lane every day.
Dancing with the bulls in any old way.
Running like a fox to keep up with me.

Chorus.

I'm on forty-five, forty-five,
Three six and Broadway,
Broadway, now Broadway,
Now Broadway, now Broadway.

Sailing

I am sailing, I am sailing,
Home again 'cross the sea.
I am sailing stormy waters,
To be near you to be free.

I am flying, I am flying,
Like a bird 'cross the sky.
I am flying passing high clouds,
To be with you to be free.

Can you hear me, can you hear me,
Thro' the dark night far away.
I am dying forever trying,
To be with you who can say.

Can you hear me, can you hear me,
Thro' the dark night far away.
I am dying, forever trying,
To be with you who can say.

We are sailing, we are sailing,
Home again 'cross the sea.
We are sailing, stormy waters,
To be near you to be free.

Oh Lord to be near you
To be free.
Oh Lord to be near you
To be free.

One More Night

One more night,
One more night.

I've been trying oh so long to let you know,
Let you know how I feel.
And if I stumble if I fall,
Just help me back so I can make you see.
Chorus:
Please give me one more night.
Give me one more night.
One more night, 'cause I can't wait forever.
Give me one more night,
Just one more night.
Oh, one more night, 'cause I can't wait forever.

I've been sitting here so long, wasting time,
Just staring at the phone.
And I was wond'ring should I call you,
Then I thought maybe you're not alone.

Chorus.

I know there'll never be a time you'll ever feel the same.
And I know it's only words.
But if you change your mind,
You know that I'll be here, and maybe we both can learn.

Chorus.

Give me one more night.
Give me just one more night.
One more night 'cause I can't wait forever.

Like a river to the sea,
I will always be with you.
And if you sail away,
I will follow you.

Give me one more night,
Give me just one more night,
Oh, one more night, 'cause I can't wait forever.

Give me just a one more night.
Give me just a one more night,
One more night. 'Cause I can't wait forever.

Give me just a one more night.
Give me just a one more night,
One more night. 'Cause I can't wait forever.

Dance Away The Heartaches

Yesterday, well it seemed so cool,
When I walked you home kissed goodnight,
I said "It's love", you said "Alright".
It's funny how I could never cry
Until tonight and you pass by,
Hand in hand with another guy,
You're dressed to kill and guess who's dying?
Chorus:

Dance away the heartaches, dance away the tears.
Dance away the heartaches , dance away the tears
Dance away.

Loneliness is a crowded room
Full of open hearts, turned to stone,
All together, all alone.
All at once my whole world had changed,
Now I'm in the dark, off the wall,
Let the strobe light up them all,
I close my eyes and dance till dawn.
Chorus:
Now I know I must walk the line,
Until I find an open door,
Off the street on to the floor.
There was I many times a fool,
I hope and pray but not too much,
Out of reach is out of touch,
All the way is far enough.

Chorus.
Dance away.
Dance away.
Dance away.
Dance away the heartaches, dance away the tears.
Dance away the heartaches, dance away the tears.
Dance away the heartaches, dance away the tears.
Dance away the heartaches, dance away the tears.

Printed in Great Britain by Printwise (Haverhill) Limited, Haverhill, Suffolk 3/98 (30340)